Wedding Dresses

FROM

The Bowes Museum
Collection

JOANNA HASHAGEN

FRIENDS
OF THE

BOWES
MUSEUM

Cover Wedding dress of 1880 *see page 24*
Left Detail of wedding dress of 1863 *see page 16*

Chairman's Foreword

T HE DRESSES in this publication are lovely. Much careful cleaning and stitching has gone on to return them to such a wonderful condition. New research has added the most interesting descriptions of people, time and place. The original photographs and fashion plates increase our enjoyment.

Joséphine Bowes' own collection of fashion magazines and her dressmaker's bills are part of the Museum's collection, but not her nineteenth century clothes. Perhaps one day Joséphine's wedding dress will turn up in another collection? Meanwhile we are grateful to all those including the most recent donors who have enabled us to add to the fabulous textile collection made by our Founders. These donations have made this publication and the *Wedding Belles* exhibition that has inspired it, possible. The dresses show the changes in fashions and taste over a one hundred and fifty year period; each one is a remarkable document of social and design history.

Viscount Eccles

Chairman, Board of Trustees

The Bowes Museum

Left One of Joséphine Bowes' fashion plates from Revue de la Mode, 1857. Hand-coloured engraving by A Adam. This magazine, published in Paris, only ran from 1857 to 1858.

Director's Acknowledgments

THE DIRECTOR wishes to thank the Friends of The Bowes Museum whose generous financial help has enabled this book to be published. We are indebted to all the donors who have given wedding dresses to the museum over the years. The collection has continued to grow and in 2003 there have been some interesting additions, including the earliest wedding dress in the collection of 1828.

There are a number of people whose contribution to this book has been invaluable and I know that Joanna Hashagen, our Keeper of Textiles, feels particularly indebted to them. Santina Levey, a textiles expert and Trustee of The Bowes Museum, has offered great encouragement and advice. The production of the handlist has involved checking past documentation relating to each dress, which was sometimes minimal. Jean Hemingway, a research volunteer from the Friends of The Bowes Museum, has worked tirelessly, painstakingly checking census returns, marriage registers and newspapers to pinpoint the name and age of the bride and the place and date of her marriage. These discoveries have provided more accurate dates for dresses in a number of cases.

We are grateful to the conservators, Dinah Jones and Caroline Rendell, particularly for Dinah's expertise in mounting the dresses on models. Without their skills, the excellent photographs by Syd Neville, our photographer, would not have been possible. Thanks are also due to Sarah Cotton, curatorial assistant, who helped with the photography and the first draft of the handlist and Jenny Lister, assistant curator, the Museum of London, who provided information on their Hartnell dress of 1928.

Finally my thanks go to Joanna Hashagen for her original idea to mount a successful exhibition of wedding dresses from The Bowes Museum collection, which has resulted in their research, conservation, photography, and the writing of this publication.

Adrian Jenkins
Director, The Bowes Museum

The moral rights of the author have been asserted
All photographs © The Bowes Museum
ISBN 0-9502375-6-6
First published in 2003 by the Friends of The Bowes Museum,
The Bowes Museum, Barnard Castle, County Durham
Designed by Barron Hatchett Design, Manchester
Printed in England

Right Original photograph showing the bride wearing the wedding dress designed by Norman Hartnell, 1928

Journal de Modes

Coiffures de Leroy, Passage de Marston 11 rue Vivienne. Fleurs de Escrcheville 28 rue
de Grammont. Dentelles de M.me Hippolyte, passage de l'Opération magasin rue de la Paix 9
Robes de Madame Reytel. Rue de la Paix 100. Mouchoirs de Chapron rue de la Paix 11
Parfumerie de la Société hygiénique. rue Vivienne 49.

Introduction

THE COSTUME COLLECTION of The Bowes Museum contains eighty wedding dresses, spanning more than a hundred and forty years of bridal fashions, from 1828 to 1969.

This catalogue has been produced to accompany a temporary exhibition, *Wedding Belles – Two Centuries of Bridal Fashion*[1], as a means of recording the holdings of the collection in a more permanent manner. By featuring illustrations of the dresses that were specially conserved and mounted for that exhibition, they will continue to be seen and enjoyed long after the dresses themselves have been returned to their long-term storage in the museum's wardrobes. Over a third of the collection is illustrated here and a hand list of the entire collection is to be found at the back of the book.

Wedding dresses, usually made of delicate materials and light coloured, are often very fragile. In the past the museum has only been able to show wedding dresses that were in a good state of preservation. Most of the bridal gowns illustrated in this catalogue have undergone conservation treatment. This has involved cleaning the dresses and some conservation stitching to support weak areas, often under the arms. They were then mounted onto the display models, which were carefully made to form the correct period shape, for photography and display. This has allowed many dresses in the museum's collection to be seen for the first time.

Wedding dresses have special significance in museum costume collections, as donors can nearly always give details about the wearer and can often provide photographs of the bride wearing the dress. In most cases it is known who the bride was, where she came from, whom she married and the date and place of the marriage. This background information, known as the provenance, is highly valued by the museum as it provides a social context for each dress.

Worn for a special celebration, wedding clothes reflect the social customs and attitudes of society. This collection reflects a wide social range, from elaborate, high society weddings in London to simpler ceremonies in the mining villages of County Durham.

They also reflect fashion, illustrating well the changing styles of the nineteenth and twentieth centuries, as wedding dresses seldom diverged from the prevailing fashion. They are presented here in a chronological order to emphasise this fashionable sequence. The wedding dress collection in The Bowes Museum is extremely comprehensive. Described as an 'excellent series'[2], costume historians over the years have noted its strengths.[3] The wedding dress collection is able to illustrate a sequence of changing styles more accurately than the main dress collection, as each dress has a known date of when it was worn and represents the current fashion of the time.

Before 1886 marriages had to take place before twelve noon and Victorian etiquette required the bride to wear the high neckline and long sleeves of daywear. It was considered correct to wear your wedding dress in the evening during the first year of your marriage. It could remain unaltered, but if worn in the second year, etiquette decreed that it should be altered to an evening style. This usually involved lowering the neckline and shortening the sleeves, making it more appropriate for eveningwear. A number of dresses in the collection reveal such alterations. Some dresses have detachable long sleeves, others have survived with two bodices, one for day and one for evening.

In the early years of the twentieth century bridal fashions began to follow evening styles, often romantically influenced by 'Grecian' or 'mediaeval' styles. Throughout the history of wedding fashions, the influence of royal brides has been keenly felt and this collection reveals those influences too.

The idea of wearing a bridal gown for one day only is a very recent one. This collection provides ample evidence that wedding dresses were worn again, either as best or evening dress. Some were kept in the family to be remodelled and worn again by a bride from a later generation.

The exclusive wearing of a special dress for just the wedding ceremony begins to appear in the later examples in this collection. The wedding dress worn in 1969 has become a specialised form of dress that no longer reflects current fashions, but is looking nostalgically at earlier styles. Today's bride can indulge in a variety of styles, many inspired by the past

White was only beginning to establish itself as the traditional colour by the beginning of the nineteenth century, and blue, grey and lilac made frequent appearances. For young women, white was also a very fashionable colour for evening and ball gowns. A white ball gown is illustrated in the fashion plate of 1858 opposite. It has a low neckline and short sleeves, contrasting with the more demure wedding dress on the left.

Stronger colours were more usual for older brides or second marriages. By the twentieth century, white had become almost universal. Before the advent of modern bleaches, 'white' referred to a range of cream and ivory shades.

In the nineteenth and early twentieth centuries, the only difference between a fashionable day dress and a wedding dress would be the colour and the richness of the material. Silk or silk satin was the usual choice but wool, or a wool and silk mix, were sometimes favoured for a winter wedding. With the advent of synthetic fabrics in the 1920s, many brides chose these latest fabrics, like rayon and viscose. By the 1960s easy-care white nylon fabrics and net were widely used for bridal wear.

Many of the dresses have their original veils, headdresses, shoes and other accessories, adding to the richness of the collection.

Joanna Hashagen Keeper of Textiles

---

[1] Exhibited at The Bowes Museum, 24 May 2003 – 18 April 2004

[2] Report on the Textiles of The Bowes Museum, Miss AM Buck, 1979

[3] *A Handbook of Costume*, Janet Arnold, Macmillan 1973, p 242;
    The Guide to Historic Costume, Karen Baclawski, Batsford, 1995, pp 224 – 229

LE CONSEILLER DES DAMES & DES DEMOISELLES

Journal d'économie domestique & de travaux d'aiguille.

159, rue Montmartre.

Paris: Un an, 10 francs. Province 12 francs.

1842

Pale gold coloured silk satin, trimmed with silk lace, silk cord and chenille tassels

This dress illustrates well the style of the early 1840s, where sleeves were decreasing in size but skirts were growing fuller, pleated into the waist There is a matching shoulder cape, trimmed with swansdown, tying with matching cord and chenille tassels. Capes were a popular choice at this time when low, wide necklines for daywear were fashionable. The lower sleeves are detachable for eveningwear. The choice of a high sheen fabric in contemporary style was perhaps influenced by Queen Victoria's white satin wedding dress of 1840.

Provenance *Worn by Hannah Bell, aged 30, only child of John Bell, a yeoman, Gill House, Romaldkirk, on 13 October 1842, for her marriage to Ralph Dent of Streatlam House, the land agent for John Bowes, co-founder of The Bowes Museum. Their son, Ralph John, born 1844, succeeded him as agent and in time became a Trustee of The Bowes Museum.*

Presented by *Mrs C G Wilcox*

Museum number *1963.773*

1849

Red and pale pink striped silk damask, trimmed with narrow braid on cuffs

Waistlines steadily lengthened during the 1840s, dipping to a sharp point at the front. The pleats, seams and the piping on the boned bodice emphasise this V-shape. The angular line of the 1840s has a smooth sloping shoulder and a tight long sleeve.

The fabric would have been very expensive and the colour is perhaps an unusual choice to be married in, but it is a cheerful choice for a November day. It has clearly been a favourite dress as it shows extensive signs of wear.

Provenance *Worn by Christiana Catherine Taylor, aged 26, of St Catherine's Parish, Gloucester, daughter of John Taylor, a gentleman, for her marriage to William Roberts, grocer, of St John the Baptist Parish, Gloucester, son of John Roberts, grocer. The marriage took place at St Mary de Lode Church, Gloucester on November 21, 1849.*

Presented by *Miss O M Perrott*
Museum number *1966.76*

1855-8

Pale blue silk, with white stripes woven *à disposition* ('to shape'), trimmed with matching silk fringe and tassels

This is a good example of how styles softened and skirts increased in width during the 1850s. The boned bodice has wide pagoda sleeves, worn with separate under sleeves. Skirts with flounces, with the design woven 'to shape', were very fashionable. They created added fullness to the skirt without adding more fabric at the waist This attractive blue had been a traditional colour for wedding dresses in the eighteenth century, when it was often teamed with silver.

Accessories

A petticoat of white cotton. A lace collar and undersleeves have been added from the Museum's collection.

Provenance

Said to have been worn by a bride or bridesmaid, a relative of Mrs Throop in Bardney or Witham, Lincoln. (See Mrs Throop's wedding dress of 1874)

Presented by Miss O E Brackenbury, granddaughter of Mrs Throop.

Museum number

1962.462

1863 & 1949

White lace, satin ribbon, and silk net with skirt flounces of Limerick lace

This is a fine example of the confections of lace and ribbon, fashionable as wedding or ball gowns in the late 1850s that can be seen in Joséphine Bowes' fashion plates. The separate boned bodice is designed for eveningwear, with short sleeves and a low neckline. Two tiers of Limerick lace, a hand embroidered machine net, make up the skirt. It had been altered slightly in 1949 with the addition of a modern lining and waistband, which were removed to return it to its original nineteenth century form. The full, gathered tiers of the skirt required the support of a crinoline to recreate the correct silhouette (the circumference of the hem measures over 5 metres).

Accessories *White cotton petticoat, pair of separate lace sleeves, pair of lace mittens, all nineteenth century.*

Provenance *Worn by Margaret Jane Trotter, aged 26, of Bishop Auckland, daughter of William Trotter, Solicitor, as a ball gown and possibly for her marriage to James E W Loft, of Healing, Lincolnshire, clergyman, son of Thomas Capel Loft (Lieutenant, 92nd Regiment) at St Andrew Auckland Parish Church, County Durham, on 8 April 1863.*

Worn again by Margaret's granddaughter, Katherine Frances Loft for her marriage to Arthur Morton in Louth, Lincolnshire, in August 1949.

Presented by *Mrs J Pearson (daughter of 1949 bride)*

Museum number *2002 .15*

1863-5

Cream ribbed silk trimmed with silk fringe and bows, edged in cream satin

The wide sleeves, a full skirt worn over a crinoline and the decorative swags and bows were fashionable features around 1863. The dressmaking is very high quality but the dress has been altered for later use; the original high round neckline has been folded inside the bodice to form a V-shape more suitable for eveningwear. The high waistline, although briefly fashionable in 1865, is an amateur alteration and the waistband of the skirt has been let out more than once, suggesting that these alterations were to accommodate pregnancy.

Provenance *Not known*

Presented by *Mrs Rawson Briggs*

Museum number *1977.68*

1875

Lilac watered silk trimmed with matching satin

The bodice is old-fashioned for 1875, by which time jacket bodices were fitting smoothly over the hips. The skirt is also wide for this date, when fullness was concentrated at the back. It is evident that the dress was altered from a late 1860s form, at which time both the fabric and colour were fashionable. It is possible that it was worn for the bride's first marriage in 1868. Lilac was also a colour suitable for half mourning.

Accessories *The lace collar and cuffs are original. A second bodice of lace with matching lilac satin trim for eveningwear.*

Provenance *Worn by Elizabeth Throop, aged 48, widow, for her marriage to William Edman, widower, a baker, both of Bardney, Lincoln on 28 October 1875.*

In 1868, Elizabeth had married Charles Throop, agent to a gentleman farmer, at Bardney. Elizabeth's father, William Cockett, was a grocer in Bardney.

Presented by
Miss O E Brackenbury (granddaughter of the bride)

Museum number *1962.461*

1877

Grey silk and alpaca, trimmed with pleated panels, lace and silk bows

By 1875 a new narrower line had emerged, which can be seen here. The skirt is worn with a bustle, emphasised by the horizontal pleats of the panel that extends below it. Pleated trimming was very popular in the 1870s as it could be more quickly produced with a sewing machine, now widely available. This dress is machine sewn but many dressmakers still preferred to handsew, particularly for special outfits, making alterations much easier. The colour grey usually denoted half-mourning.

Maker *Georgina Watson, the bride.*

Provenance *Worn at Lanchester in 1877 by Georgina Watson, aged 18, for her marriage to William Short, grocer, later manager of the 'Co-op', Esh, County Durham.*

Presented by *Mrs Richardson (bride's daughter)*

Museum number *1970.172*

1880

Cream silk trimmed with satin bows, silk net, artificial flowers and pleated frills and lace at hem

This one-piece dress is in the style known as the Princess line, which achieved a new sheath-like silhouette and was the height of fashion in 1880. The front ruched panel with the line of bows enhances the vertical effect. Inside the skirt are tapes to tie at the back to tighten the skirt around the legs and to create the elaborate bustle effect. Trains were no longer fashionable for day wear, but were still worn for weddings and in the evenings.

Accessories *Wreath of orange blossom*

Provenance *Worn by Mary Adshead, aged 21, of Ulgham Grange, Bedlington, Northumberland for her marriage to her cousin Patrick Freeman, aged 35, farmer, of Newcastle on 26 August, 1880. The couple farmed 190 acres at Seaton Delaval.*

Presented by *Miss S Mutum,*

Museum number *1964.894*

1889-1892

White corded silk trimmed with chiffon, bronze and silver coloured beads and pearls, cream lace frill at hem

This dress illustrates the new fashionable line apparent from 1889, with a plainer narrow skirt trailing into a train without a bustle or drapery. In response, bodices become more elaborate. Bridal wear was no exception, becoming highly decorated. Sleeves were growing larger and were another area for added opulence. The lower parts of the original sleeves were removed for eveningwear, but have now been re-attached.

Provenance *Worn by a doctor's daughter from Allendale, Northumberland, for her wedding.*

Presented by *Mrs Todd, Darlington (granddaughter of bride)*

Museum number *1964-847*

1891

Jacket and waistcoat of brown silk plush

Maker *Robert Hedley & Co Mantle Warehouse, Bishop Auckland.*

During the 1880s and 1890s women were beginning to adopt more practical forms of day dress as increasing numbers were going out to work. They tended to incorporate masculine elements, and these 'Tailor-made' costumes were considered very smart. 'Woman's World' magazine of 1889 stated that ' such costumes are worn in London at the smartest weddings and afternoon parties'. For the less well off, it would have been a very practical choice. The waistcoat consists of the front panels only and it is attached to the jacket at the side seams. Said to have been made from Hatters Plush, costing 35 shillings a yard and worn with a silk skirt and a hat by the bride. Plush is a type of velvet with a long shaggy pile, very characteristic of the 1880s, when furnishing- type fabrics were often adopted for fashionable dress.

Accessories *The skirt of red silk is added from the museum collection. Originally worn with a fine wool skirt, terracotta coloured; plush hat of same colour with high crown and narrow brim trimmed with feathers; fur collar and muff of red beaver.*

Provenance *Worn by Annie Lynas, aged 31, daughter of Andrew Lynas, engine driver, of Fir Tree, North Bedburn, County Durham, for her marriage to Joseph Featherstone Ellwood, coal miner, and son of a farmer, of High Moor Hill Hamsterley, County Durham. It is thought that the wedding celebrations took place at the Duke of York's public house at Fir Tree, which, at the 1891 Census, was held by the bride's sister, Jane, and brother-in-law, Benjamin Carter, who witnessed the marriage at the C of E Chapel at Hamsterley on 22 March, 1891.*

Presented by *Miss Ellwood (daughter of bride)*

Museum number *1971.113.5*

1895

Ivory silk, trimmed with satin ribbon, chiffon and lace

Maker *Miss Laking, a local dressmaker from Louth, who also made the bridesmaids' dresses. Altered to an evening dress by C. Watson and Company, Bishop Auckland, after 1903.*

The wedding photograph reveals the original form of the dress, with large leg of mutton sleeves, which were the height of fashion in 1895. They were replaced with tight sleeves and pleated chiffon in 1903, reflecting a new softer style and lighter fabrics.

Accessories *Pair of sleeves, the lower half of the original sleeves, designed to be detachable; shoes, cream silk with ribbon bows; stockings, cream silk; silk cord with tassel and clip to lift the hem.*

Further notes *Extract from description in the Auckland Times and Herald:*

FASHIONABLE MARRIAGE – the bride's wedding gown was of ivory ondine silk, trimmed with old Honiton lace, chiffon, and orange blossom, and she wore a plain white tulle veil fastened with orange blossom, and carried a shower bouquet of roses and jessamine. The bridesmaids were gowned in cream silk zephyr with yokes and sashes of pale blue silk, and wore large picture hats trimmed with white tips and pale blue velvet rosettes and carried shower bouquets of roses and forget-me-nots.

Provenance *Worn by Miss Edith Violet Allison, aged 25, daughter of the town clerk of Louth, for her marriage to Mr Percy John Martin Loft, a solicitor, at Holy Trinity Church, Louth, Lincolnshire, on Tuesday, 6 August, 1895 at 11.30 am. Percy Loft joined his cousin in the firm of Trotter, Bruce and Trotter of Bishop Auckland, County Durham in 1903.*

Presented by *Mrs B Wilson (daughter of Mr Loft's housekeeper).*

Museum number *1997.28*

1901

Brown silk and cream guipure lace over cream silk trimmed with satin ribbon and diamanté clips

This dress was worn twice as a wedding dress, first in 1876 and then by the bride's daughter in 1901. There is evidence of extensive alteration and the 1876 form has been completely obliterated by the re-modelling in 1901. The boned bodice with a high neckline and square yoke, in-filled with lace, is typical of Edwardian fashions. The colour may have been chosen for its general usefulness, as the dress has been well worn. Working brides were advised, in magazines of the day, to choose practical outfits in dark colours, to be worn with hats rather than veils.

Accessories *Hat, plaited straw with brim, trimmed with cream silk chiffon and ostrich feathers, 1901. A second hat of plaited straw, trimmed with velvet and satin ribbons, said to have been worn by the first bride in 1876.*

Provenance *Worn by Margaret Henderson, aged 23, daughter of John Henderson, foreman boiler smith, Seaham Harbour, County Durham, for her marriage to Edward Childs, house painter, at St John's Church, Seaham Harbour on 27 March, 1901. Childs was born at Great Yarmouth, but had moved to Seaham with his family; his father was a butler. The dress was first worn in 1876, by Margaret's mother, Harriet Mason, aged 23, daughter of a mariner, Seaham Harbour, for her marriage to John Henderson, of Sunderland.*

Presented by *Miss E Childs (granddaughter and daughter of brides)*

Museum number *1964.838, 1964.839*

1912

Ivory silk satin and silk chiffon, trimmed with point de gaze lace, artificial pearls, beads and silver metal thread

Maker *Lucile, 23 Hanover Square, London.*

Lucile was the leading couturier of the day, with salons in London, Paris and New York. The draped 'Grecian' style is typical of the romanticism of Lucile's designs. The mastery of this dress, which appears so simple, is in the cutting and the construction which has an under bodice with a deep, boned waistband and intricate concealed fastenings.

Accessories *Veil of fine silk tulle with a wreath of artificial laurel leaves and orange blossom. Separate train, attached at the shoulders, silk chiffon softly gathered into bands of lace. Court train, silk chiffon and silk satin, longer and more elaborately trimmed with lace embroidered with silver bugle beads. It was customary for society brides to be presented at court after marriage, wearing their wedding dress with the addition of a full-length court train.*

Provenance *Worn by Linda Morritt, aged 26, daughter of Robert Morritt of Rokeby Park, Barnard Castle, for her marriage to William Rhodes Moorhouse, a pioneer aviator, at St Paul's, Knightsbridge, London in 1912.*

Further notes *On their wedding cake was a small silver model of an exact replica of the aeroplane designed and flown by William. After a brief stay at the Savoy Hotel, their honeymoon was spent making the first trans-channel flight in a three-seater aircraft. William was awarded the first VC for bravery in the air, after he was killed in a solo-bombing raid in 1915. Linda Rhodes Moorhouse lived at Mortham Towers, Barnard Castle*

Presented by *Mrs Diana Cavendish, Mrs S Ryle-Hodges and Princess Iris Wittgenstein (nieces of bride).*

Museum number *1989.26*

1919

Ivory silk and wool mix, trimmed with self-fabric frills, covered buttons and lace

A shorter skirt illustrates the practical changes in style during the First World War. The simple bodice is cut in one with the sleeves, with a crossover front. 'Vogue' magazine in 1919 advised that 'the bridal gown of today… must have an air of simplicity to match the simple charm of these young girls'. The lace used for the wired collar and on the shoulders is an appropriate choice, incorporating heart motifs. It is a machine-made lace of good quality.

Accessories *A circular veil of embroidered machine net with wreath of orange blossom; shoes, white satin with bar fastening and diamanté button; stockings, white silk; handkerchief, white silk with deep lace edging; length of broad white satin ribbon probably used to tie bouquet.*

Provenance *Not known. Small pieces of confetti were found in the hem.*

Presented by *Mrs Dowson*
Museum number *1965.154*

1921

Cream crêpe-backed satin and chiffon, trimmed with seed pearls and beads Lined with crêpe de chine, with lace and ribbon trim at neck

Maker *Miss Grey Ltd, 9, 11, & 13 Brook Street, Hanover Square, London W1.*

An intricately constructed dress in expensive fabrics which create a soft, draped style. The skirt is the new, shorter length and the train falls from the waist. The attached corsage of artificial roses and orange blossom is a rare survivor and suggests that this dress was worn only once.

Provenance *Worn by Frieda Victoria Annie Stephenson, of Throckley, for her marriage to Major John Fleming Lockhart DSO of Hexham, at Hexham Parish Church, Northumberland on 16 June, 1921. They both belonged to well-known military and landowning families in Northumberland.*

Further notes *Extracts from a contemporary newspaper:*

The service at the marriage of Colonel Lockhart's gallant son was distinctly impressive. It was fully choral, Abbey choir being in attendance... the bride wore a handsome dress of cream satin with train of brocade, covered with old lace and she had a bridal veil of tulle. She carried a sheaf of cream roses. Her ornament was a pearl and diamond pendant, gift of the bridegroom... Major and Mrs Lockhart left for the South of France. The bride's going away gown was of brown and fawn crêpe de chine, with cloak to match, with which she wore a hat of brown and gold lace. Colonel Lockhart's gifts to his soldier son included Sunniside Estate.

Presented by *J S Stephenson, (nephew of the bride)*

Museum number *1979.42.1*

1926

Cream silk satin crêpe with machine-made lace yoke and skirt panels over pale peach silk, trimmed with diamanté, pearls, silver beads and silver lace

Wedding dresses became more like fashionable evening dresses in the 1920s, and skirts steadily became shorter. Pastel colours, particularly blue or peach, were popular.

Maker *A London dressmaker, to the design of the bride.*

Accessories *Underslip of peach silk, trimmed with broad bands of lace.*

Provenance *Worn by Norah Macoun Wells, aged 29, of London, for her marriage to Reginald Frederick Spalding, of Newcastle, at Hampstead Parish Church, London on 15 June, 1926. The bride had been a nurse in Malta; the groom was a director of F W Dobson & Co Ltd, Darlington.*

Presented by *Mrs Bridget Westmacott (granddaughter of bride)*

Museum number *1993.17*

1927

White fine cotton net tunic, trimmed with silver lamé, over white satin rayon, with silver lamé belt

This low-waisted style, with deep long sleeves and a silver girdle was part of the 'medieval' look which remained popular with brides throughout the 1920s. Silver lamé was popularised by two royal brides. Princess Mary, in 1922, wore a silver lamé tunic-style gown with a transparent over-tunic, which set the pattern for this dress. In 1923, Lady Elizabeth Bowes Lyon's dress displayed bands of silver lamé embroidered with seed pearls.

Maker *Miss Strand, purchased from H Binns of Sunderland.*

Accessories *Drawstring bag of silver lamé.*

Provenance *Worn by Sarah Phyllis Hudson, for her marriage to Wilton Legender Milburn at the Wesleyan Chapel, Sunderland on 8 September, 1927.*

Presented by *Mrs Whittaker of Sunderland (niece of bride)*

Museum number *1979.6*

1928

Ivory silk satin and silk net, with cut-out flower shapes with silk net infill, each trimmed with silver lace and embroidered with bugle beads and a pearl in the centre of each flower

This drop-waisted style has deep mediaeval-style sleeves. The design of graduating five-petalled flowers became a favourite Hartnell motif and this is one of the earliest examples of its use. Hartnell was at the beginning of a glittering career, creating exquisite gowns for the cream of society.

West Hartlepool, of the well-known ship-owning family. The wedding took place at St Margaret's, Westminster and the reception was held at Warwick House, St James's, London, on Tuesday, 24 July 1928.

Further notes

Extracts from the Northern Daily Mail, 24 July 1928:

St Margaret's Westminster, the scene of so many fashionable weddings, again attracted many notable people today... the wedding was a sequel to a romance that began two years ago at Lord Rothmere's Villa at Deauville... It is the intention of Mr and Mrs Jock Ropner to make their home in West Hartlepool.

Maker *Norman Hartnell, 10 Bruton Street, London*

Accessories *Train, silk net, silver metal thread at border, with applied satin flowers, each trimmed with silver lace and embroidered with bugle beads and a pearl in the centre of each flower. Veil, silk net, with band of orange blossom. Headdress, tiara of silver lace, with diamanté and pearls.*

Provenance *Worn by Joan Redhead, daughter of Lady Lacon and Mr William Redhead, for her marriage to John W Ropner, son of William Ropner, of*

A similar dress by Hartnell, in pink satin, was worn to the 'Dream of Fair Women' Charity Ball at Claridges in February 1928 and is in the Museum of London (28.44). In 1933 he made another version for Margaret Whigham, who became the Duchess of Argyll (Victoria and Albert Museum, T.836-1974). Similar flowers appeared on Princess Elizabeth's elaborately embroidered wedding dress of 1947.

Presented by *Mrs Joan Ropner (bride).*

Museum number *1981.8*

1932

Deep powder blue silk georgette crêpe trimmed with lace

The dress is constructed as a double layer with bias cut panels and a floating panel from the left hip. This asymmetrical style is a good example of a fashionable afternoon dress. Silk crêpe or chiffon with a matt-finish was favoured more than shiny satins. Hats, not veils, were worn with these coloured day dresses. It was thought to have been bought at Binns in Darlington or in Newcastle.

Provenance *Worn by Eva Stephenson, of Tursdale House, Croxdale, for her marriage to George Graham Hankey, farmer, Witton Gilbert, on 27 April 1932 at Croxdale Church, County Durham.*

Presented by *Mrs E Perkins (daughter of the bride)*

Museum number *1998.304.5*

1934

Cream silk panne velvet

This long, bias cut gown is a good example of how wedding dresses were diverging from fashionable daywear in the 1930s. Brides turned to eveningwear and romantic, softly draped styles in luxurious fabrics.

Maker *Possibly by the bride, as she was a dressmaker for Binn's in Sunderland, and it is known that she made the trousseau. The shoes and possibly the dress may have been bought ready-made from a shop in Sunderland called Lance Defty.*

Accessories *Dress clip, chrome metal and diamanté in an art deco design; shoes, white satin. The trousseau consists of matching pyjamas, under-slip, drawers and camisole of ivory satin trimmed with pink machine-made lace.*

Provenance *Worn by Eleanor Jane Thomlinson, aged 24, a blacksmith's daughter, of South Hylton, Sunderland for her marriage to John Robert Raine, aged 34, an LNER engine driver, son of a miner, at St Mary's, South Hylton on 24 September 1934.*

Presented by *Mrs T Hodgson (bride's daughter)*

Museum number *1998.308*

1938

Cream lace made of a synthetic fibre, embroidered with silver bugle beads, cream rayon underslip

The cowl neckline and clinging drapery are typical for this date, but the fabric is an unusual, high quality lace fabric, made from an extruded synthetic fibre. It is embroidered to fit the shape of the dress and a good example of the 'jewelled' simplicity of late 1930s wedding dresses, influenced by the glamour of Hollywood.

Accessories *Veil, two layers of silk net, with cream satin bow applied on lower edge; head-dress of artificial lily of the valley by Halbur Veils, with original box. Wedding album and wedding photograph in silver frame.*

Provenance *Worn by Ruby Pattinson for her marriage to Dr William Stuart Gale, on 7 September 1938 at Low Fell, Gateshead. Dr Gale was a General Medical Practitioner in Teesdale.*

Presented by *Mr D Gale, Mrs S Hunter and Mrs P Hopley (children of the bride)*

Museum number *1999.184*

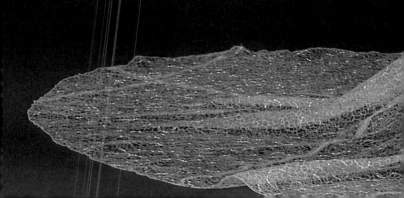

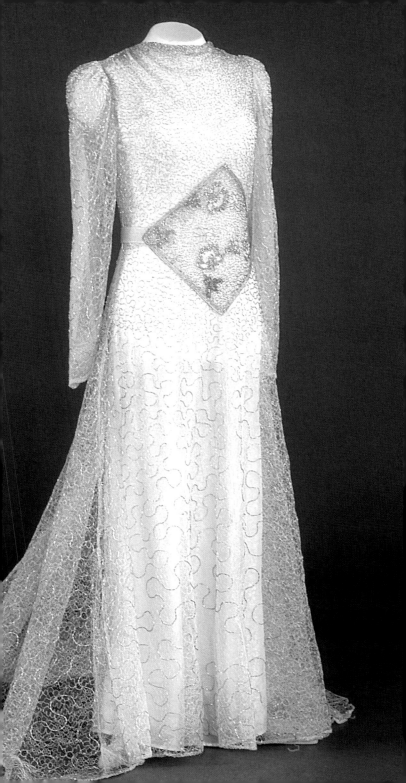

1940

White rayon satin with machine quilted collar and shoulder pads

The fashionable padded shoulder was adopted for wedding dresses and this extreme example also has a padded stand–up collar, in what the bride described as 'Elizabethan' style. It is a good example of how a couture model was interpreted by the cheaper end of the trade. Choice of mass-produced, ready-made garments increased enormously in the 1930s. Rayon fabric was a cheaper alternative to silk and it is a colder shade of white. The white wedding had become firmly established by the end of the 1930s.

Accessories *Veil, white net with chain stitch design in floss silk with applied white rayon satin horseshoes; headdress of artificial flowers and mistletoe, from 'Charles', Coney Street, York.*

Provenance *Worn by Audrey Grosgert, aged 31, of Ferryhill, County Durham, for her marriage to John George Pattinson, who worked at Trimdon Grange coke ovens , son of a colliery engineer from Ashington, Northumberland, at St Luke's Church, Ferryhill, County Durham, on 20 January 1940 at 3 pm. The bride had an aunt in York who had made her clothes as a child and helped choose the wedding dress from 'Charles', Coney Street, York.*

Further notes *Extract from the Auckland Chronicle, 25 January 1940:*

The bride has for 11 years been secretary of the Mainsforth Women's Institute, is a member of the Ferryhill and District Amateur Operatic Society, and a member of the Ferryhill Hospitals Aid Committee… she wore a period gown of white satin with a Medici collar… the reception was held at Broom Labour Hall, Ferryhill.

An identical dress is in the collection of the Imperial War Museum, London, worn by a bride in 1939. (IWM 97/ 24/3)

Presented by *Mrs Audrey Pattinson (bride)*

Museum number *1997.12.2*

1946

Ivory rayon satin, self-fabric coloured buttons

A fluid well cut dress with a softly gathered bodice and long sleeves pointed at the wrist The long gored skirt sweeps elegantly into a train. It was bought second-hand. Wedding dresses were difficult to obtain during the war, so other alternatives were sought to save coupons: making your own in furnishing fabrics or lace, which were unrestricted by coupons; wearing your mother's or grandmother's dress; choosing a new tailored suit; or, buying second-hand. In 1946, a new 'wedding gown in ivory rayon satin' cost seven coupons or £15 and 13 shillings. Hiring of dresses only began after the war.

Provenance *Worn by Florence Marina Wickham aged 40, of Thunderbridge, Huddersfield, for her marriage to Arthur William Holmes, an ICI chemist, at Stockton Parish Church on 12 January 1946. She was a typist and lived in Eaglescliffe before her marriage.*

Presented by *Mr R H A Nellist and Mr R Holmes on behalf of Mrs F M Holmes (bride)*

Museum number *1992.14*

1947

White and silver lamé silk brocade in a floral design

The slender, elegant 1930s line, achieved by bias cutting, continued to be worn by wartime brides. The simple line is relieved by the draped and crossed fabric on the bodice. This is an expensive fabric and the dress may have been first worn in the 1930s or the fabric saved from before the war. In 1934 Princess Marina wore a very similar silver brocade gown that had a lasting influence on society brides.

Accessories *Veil, silk net and separate train, which had been cut off to make the dress more suitable for eveningwear.*

Provenance *Worn by Anne Milvain, daughter of Lieutenant Colonel R Milvain, Eglingham Hall, Northumberland, for her marriage*

to Lieutenant Colonel William Innes Watson, solicitor, Spring Lodge, Barnard Castle, on Tuesday, 19 August 1947 at St Andrews, Heddon-on-the-Wall, Northumberland.

Further notes *Extracts from the Teesdale Mercury, 27 August, 1947:*

The bride wore a white and silver lamé tightly fitting dress, with gathered bodice and train of the same material, cut in one with the skirt. She had an ivory tulle veil held in place with velvet flowers and wore a diamond necklace, the gift of the bridegroom. She carried a bouquet of stephanotis. The honeymoon is being spent in Sweden. The bride travelled in a dress of powder blue crêpe with hat to match and blue fox cape. On their return they will live at Spring Lodge, Barnard Castle.

Presented by *Colonel W. Watson (husband of the bride)*

Museum number *1984.20*

1954

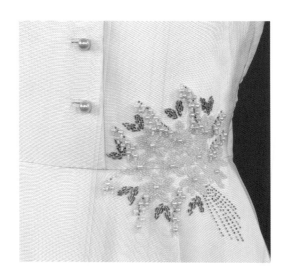

Cream corded silk with embroidered flower design of pearls, seed pearls, silver beads and diamanté

Maker *Donald Graham, London.*

This formal gown has all the elegance of Dior's New Look of 1947, which was so influential in the early 1950s. It is the 'A' line with a tight, fitted bodice, a horizontal pleat to emphasise the hip-line and a full, long skirt.

It was said to have cost £30.

Accessories *Headdress, pearl flowers and diamanté, in coronet style.*

Provenance *Worn by an Oxford undergraduate for her marriage to an Oxford don in April 1954. The donor wished that the bride and groom remained anonymous.*

Presented by *Mrs H Newton-Wilson*

Museum number *1963.539*

1955

Cream cotton lace, trimmed with bow and diamanté buckle, piped and lined with cream rayon

As short evening dresses became fashionable, the popularity of short white wedding dresses increased. This example has a characteristic wide skirt made fuller with stiffened under-layers, sloping shoulders and a shapely, fitted bodice. A bolero style short jacket was often worn, either of semi-transparent fabric or matching the wedding dress. This dress was worn with a net jacket of this type, which has not survived. It may have been made by the bride, as she made wedding dresses for others.

Accessories *Square veil of white net; a Juliet cap of cream velvet trimmed with sequins; shoes, white suede, open-toed, by 'Merrywalkers'; good luck horseshoe, silver cardboard and rayon ribbon; photographs, marriage certificate and telegram.*

Provenance *Worn by Violet Murton, aged 32, a machinist from Crook, for her marriage to Ernest Watson, aged 43, an electrical engineer inspector, of Witton-le-Wear, at St Paul's Church, Hunwick, County Durham on 3 December 1955.*

Presented by *Mrs Jennifer Hopps (bridesmaid, niece and goddaughter of bride)*

Museum number *1997.11*

1963

White acetate satin, described by the bride as 'peau de soie'

This is a sheath dress, the fashionable sleek shape of the early 1960s, which was widely adopted for wedding dresses. They were distinguished by their plain simplicity and a new 'whiteness' attainable only in synthetic fabrics. The flat front, in an unbroken line from neck to hem, is influenced by Princess Alexandra's dress, worn in April of that year. A train is attached at the back waist. It was bought from Kendal Milne & Co, Manchester.

Accessories *Short veil of four layers of nylon net; pillbox headdress, of matching satin, decorated with pearls and rhinestones.*

Provenance *Worn by Sandra McLellan of Bramhall, Cheshire for her marriage to Peter Greenhalgh, teacher at Barnard Castle School, at St Nicholls Parish Church, Bramhall on 17 August 1963.*

Presented by *Mr and Mrs P Greenhalgh (bride and groom)*

Museum number *1979.52*

1969

White nylon jersey

Maker 'The Bridal Shop', Leeds, to the bride's own design.

The late 1960s saw a more romantic, nostalgic mood in wedding design. This dress illustrates perfectly the 'little girl' look mixed with nostalgia for 'Victoriana', with the pin-tucked bodice, high collar and flounced skirt. From this time forward most brides have looked to past styles and the long white dress, worn for one day only, has become the convention.

Accessories The flower bonnet shown on the photograph has not survived, but was a popular alternative to a veil in the 1960s.

Provenance Worn by Judith Hood, university student, daughter of William Hood, painting conservator, The Bowes Museum, for her marriage to David Graham Chibbet, who worked at the British Museum, on 26 July 1969 at St Cuthbert's Church, Darlington.

Presented by Mr and Mrs W Hood (parents of the bride)

Museum number 1981.53

HAND LIST

1828

Fabric Fawn silk with figured and voided leaf design trimmed with satin ribbon **Associated items** Lace veil, tortoiseshell hair comb **Provenance** Worn by Isabella Davison (19), bride of Thomas Forster of Burradon Hall, on 24 June 1828 at Morpeth, Northumberland **Presented by** Miss M M Forster **Museum number** 2003.2332.1-3 (CST.3.280-2)

1842 see page 11

Fabric Pale gold coloured satin with matching shoulder cape **Provenance** Worn by Hannah Bell (30), bride of Ralph Dent of Streatlam House on 13 October 1842 at Romaldkirk Parish Church, County Durham **References** Karen Baclawski, *The Guide to Historic Costume*, 1995, page 225 **Presented by** Mrs C G Wilcox **Museum number** 1963-773 a, b & c (CST.742) ✿

1849 see page 12

Fabric Red and pale pink silk damask **Provenance** Worn by Christiana Catherine Taylor (26), bride of William Roberts on 21 November 1849 at Saint Mary de Lode Church, Gloucester **References** Karen Baclawski, *The Guide to Historic Costume*, 1995, page 225. **Presented by** Miss O M Perrot (granddaughter) **Museum number** 1966-76 (CST.1122) ✿

c.1850

Fabric Cotton muslin printed and woven with a checked design, in cream and brown **Associated items** Copy of wedding and birth certificates **Provenance** Said to be the wedding dress of Mary Oliver (24), of Boldron, near Barnard Castle, bride of Robert Jackson, shipwright of Sunderland on 12 May 1875 at Startforth Parish Church. The dress is in an earlier style and could be the wedding dress of her mother Mary, married circa 1850 **Presented by** Mrs Mellersh (granddaughter) **Museum number** 1998.10.1 (CST.3.196)

1852

Fabric Cream silk with figured leaf design, jacket bodice trimmed with silk fringe **Associated items** Cream silk evening bodice **Provenance** Worn in Milton, Dorset by Anna Attwater bride of William Miller, yeoman farmer on 21 April 1852 **Presented by** Mrs E Law **Museum number** 2003.2334 (CST.3.287)

1855

Fabric White silk jacket bodice of wedding dress, trimmed with silk ribbon **Provenance** Worn by Emily Berkeley for her marriage to Simon Thomas Scrope of Danby Hall, Wensleydale on 30 October 1855 at Spetchley, Worcestershire **Presented by** Mr C R Scrope **Museum number** 1963.885 (CST.754) ✿

1855-8 see page 15

Fabric Pale blue silk, woven with white stripes 'à disposition' **Associated items** Petticoat, white cotton **Provenance** Said to have been worn as a bride or bridesmaid by a relative of Mrs Throop at Bardney or Witham, Lincoln **Presented by** Miss O E Brackenbury **Museum number** 1962-462 (CST.410, 411) ✿

1863-5 see page 19

Fabric Cream ribbed silk, satin and silk fringe **Presented by** Mrs Rawson-Briggs **Museum number** 1977.68 (CST.2.319) ✿

1863 & 1949 see page 16

Fabric White lace, satin ribbon, silk net and Limerick lace flounces **Associated items** White cotton petticoat **Provenance** First worn by Margaret Jane Trotter (26), of Bishop Auckland, daughter of William Trotter, solicitor, as a ball gown and possibly for her marriage to Reverend James E W Loft, on 8 April 1863 at Saint Andrews, Auckland, County Durham; later worn by Margaret's granddaughter, Katherine Frances Loft, for her marriage to Arthur Morton, in August 1949, at Louth, Lincolnshire **Presented by** Mrs Pearson (daughter of 1949 bride) **Museum number** 2002.15.1-4 (CST.3.273 a-d) ✿

1870

Fabric Light brown silk edged with satin trimmed with silk fringe **Associated items** Yardage shawl, wool, woven design, known as 'Kirking' shawl, Paisley or Edinburgh, 1820-1835, said to have been worn with wedding dress in 1870 **Presented by** Mrs J Dearnley **Museum number** 1966-155 (CST.1188)

1870

Fabric Fawn silk and alpaca trimmed with bright blue satin **Provenance** The Going Away dress of Eliza Oldfield, bride of Reverend George William Butler, curate in Durham city **Presented by** Mrs C Stewart (granddaughter) **Museum number** 1967.354 (CST.1356)

1872

Fabric Bright aniline blue silk, trimmed black velvet ribbon and fringe **Associated items** Hymn sheet found in pocket **Provenance** Worn by Matilda Louise Quarmby (18), dressmaker, of Linthwaite, Yorkshire **Presented by** Miss C Quarmby (daughter) **Museum number** 1977.24.1 (CST.2.263)

1875 *see page 20*
Fabric Lilac watered silk, trimmed satin
Associated items Lace collar and cuffs,
evening bodice, lace with matching satin trim
Provenance Worn by Elizabeth Throop
(48), widow, for her second marriage to
William Edman, widower, a baker, both of
Bardney on October 28 1875 at Saint Mary
le Wigford Parish Church, Lincolnshire
Presented by Miss O E Brackenbury
(granddaughter of bride) **Museum
number** 1962-461 a, c (CST.405, 407) ✿

1876
Fabric Cream ribbed silk, with diagonal bands
of cream satin **Maker** James N Clarkson &
Son, Silk Mercers and General Drapers, 19
Bridge Street, Whitby **Provenance** Worn
by Mary Thomasina Clarkson (28), daughter
of James Clarkson, bride of John Annet of
Northumberland on 31 August 1876 at Saint
Mary's Abbey, Whitby **References** Karen
Baclawski, *The Guide to Historic Costume*, 1995,
page 226, figures 264a and 264b
Presented by Miss S Mutum **Museum
number** 1964.887 (CST.961)

1877
Fabric Cream silk satin, trimmed Honiton
lace **Associated items** Veil, orange
blossom, gloves, lace-edged handkerchief
Provenance Worn in Ireland by Agnes
(23), the bride of Charles Hunting, a
steamship owner and ship broker, later
of Slaley Hall, Hexham, Northumberland
Presented by Mrs A Skipwith (daughter)
Museum number 1967.93-7 (CST.1261-5)

1877 *see page 23*
Fabric Grey silk and alpaca, trimmed
with pleated panels, lace and silk bows
Maker Georgina Watson, the bride
Provenance Worn at Lanchester by
Georgina Watson (18), bride of William
Short, grocer, later manager of the Co-op at
Esh, County Durham **Presented by** Mrs
B Richardson (daughter) **Museum
number** 1970.172 (CST.1658) ✿

1877-8
Fabric Pink-grey fine wool, trimmed with
ruched satin, satin ribbon and Bedfordshire
lace **Provenance** Wedding dress worn by
donor's grandmother **References** Joanna
Hashagen, *Wedding Dresses 1870-1930*, The
Bowes Museum, 1994; Karen Baclawski, *The
Guide to Historic Costume*, 1995, front cover
illustration **Presented by** Miss E Frankland
(granddaughter) **Museum number** 1968-77
(CST.1403)

1878
Fabric Shawl only, cream wool plush, woven
with grey and black lines **Associated
items** Copy of marriage certificate;
original photograph, newspaper accounts

Provenance Worn by Mary Anna Pease
(33), Quaker, granddaughter of Edward
'Railway' Pease of Darlington, bride of
Jonathan Backhouse Hodgkin, bank director,
on 24 April 1878 at Friends Meeting House,
Darlington **Presented by** Miss L Hodgkin
Museum number 1993.26.1 (CST.3.73)

1880 *see page 24*
Fabric Cream silk trimmed with satin bows,
silk net, artificial flowers and pleated frills and
lace at hem **Associated items** Wreath of
artificial orange blossom **Provenance** Worn
by Mary Adshead (21), bride of her cousin
Patrick Freeman, a farmer, of Newcastle
upon Tyne on 26 August 1880 at Ulgham,
Northumberland **Presented by** Miss S
Mutum **Museum number** 1964-894 a & b
(CST.966-7) ✿

1881
Fabric Cream ribbed silk trimmed with
lace **Maker** Lewis and Allenby, London
Associated items Dress, yellow silk, thought
to be part of trousseau, with photograph by
Vuccino showing it being worn in Bombay
in 1883 **Provenance** Worn at Islington,
London by Jane Mountford (38), bride of
Lieutenant Colonel Wellington Gray IMS, later
Principal of Grant's Medical College, Bombay
References Joanna Hashagen, *Wedding
Dresses 1870-1930*, The Bowes Museum, 1994
Presented by Mrs Charlotte Bunney,
on behalf of Ellen Hatfield Gray (bride's
daughter) **Museum number** 1972.53.11&12
(CST.1.201-2)

1889-1892 *see page 26*
Fabric White corded silk trimmed with
chiffon and beads **Provenance** Worn
by a doctor's daughter from Allendale,
Northumberland **Presented by** Mrs Todd
(granddaughter) **Museum number** 1964-847
(CST.955) ✿

1890
Fabric Cream satin, trimmed with lace
and ribbon bows **Associated items** Pair
of long lace sleeves removed from dress
Presented by Miss Hall **Museum
number** 1966.192 (CST.1211)

1891 *see page 29*
Fabric Jacket and waistcoat of brown silk
plush. **Maker** R Hedley & Company, Bishop
Auckland **Provenance** Worn by Annie
Lynas (31), bride of Joseph Featherstone
Ellwood, a coal miner on 22 March 1891
at Hamsterley, Bishop Auckland. Originally
worn with terracotta coloured fine wool
skirt, plush hat and beaver fur collar and muff
Presented by Miss Ellwood (daughter)
Museum number 1971.113.5 (CST.1.147) ✿

1895 *see page 30*
Fabric Ivory silk, trimmed with satin ribbon,
chiffon and lace **Maker** Miss Laking. Altered to

an evening dress by C Watson and Company, Bishop Auckland, after 1903 **Associated items** Pair of matching long sleeves, skirt lifter, stockings, shoes, photograph, newspaper cuttings **Provenance** Worn by Miss Edith Violet Allison (25), bride of Mr Percy John Martin Loft, a solicitor, on 6 August 1895, at Holy Trinity Church, Louth, Lincolnshire **Presented by** Mrs B Wilson (daughter of Mr Loft's housekeeper) **Museum number** 1997.28.1-3 (CST.3.161-3) ✿

1896
Fabric Cream figured satin, trimmed with beads and lace **Maker** James Coxon & Company, Ladies Tailors, Newcastle-upon-Tyne **Associated items** Veil, orange blossom, shoes, original photograph **Provenance** Worn by Annie Mathilda Bigland (33) of Bishop Auckland, bride of Joseph Fryer, coal owner, on 29 July at the Friends Meeting House, Bishop Auckland. They were Quakers and lived at Smelt House, Howden-le-Wear, County Durham **References** Karen Baclawski, The Guide to Historic Costume, 1995, page 226-228, figure 265 **Presented by** Mrs Doris Carew-Shaw (daughter) **Museum number** 1989.11.1-3 (CST.2.880-2)

1897
Fabric White satin, trimmed with chiffon and lace **Associated items** Veil and orange blossom **Provenance** Worn by Mary Ellen (27), daughter of Eli Mallinson, woollen manufacturer, Linthwaite, Huddersfield, bride of Arthur Broadbent, printer/manager, Huddersfield, in June 1897 at Linthwaite Wesleyan Chapel **Presented by** Miss Broadbent **Museum number** 1959.122a & b (CST.305)

1898
Fabric White satin damask and silver brocade, trimmed with lace, sequins and pearls **Maker** Buckmaster, 47 Sloane Street, London **Provenance** Worn at Oundle, Northamptonshire by Eveline Lucy Menzies (25), bride of Arthur Marmaduke Whitaker, a landowner near Ripon **Presented by** Miss Whitaker (daughter) **Museum number** 1962.39 (CST.1698)

1898
Fabric Cream silk brocade, with self-coloured floral design, net sleeves and collar, trimmed with pearls and diamanté **Provenance** Worn by Laura Louise Dickinson (26), bride of Sir John Esplen, consulting engineer, of Richmond, Yorkshire on 26 January at Sunderland **References** Joanna Hashagen, Wedding Dresses 1870-1930, The Bowes Museum, 1994 **Presented by** Lady Peter Hoare (daughter) **Museum number** 1962-502 (CST.438)

c.1900
Fabric Cream satin and spotted voile

trimmed with pleated chiffon, beads and pearls **Associated items** Veil, silk net; long gloves, white kid **Presented by** Miss Hall **Museum number** 1966.193-5 (CST.1212-14)

1900
Fabric Cream satin and chiffon, lace collar embroidered with sequins **Associated items** White kid shoes by Derry and Toms, Kensington High Street, London **Provenance** Worn by donor's mother **Presented by** Miss A M C Reilly (daughter) **Museum number** 1958.17, 1970.261 (CST.845, 1699)

1901 altered from wedding dress of 1876, see page 33
Fabric Brown silk and cream lace over cream silk trimmed with satin ribbon and diamanté clips **Associated items** Hat, plaited straw, trimmed with velvet and satin ribbons, worn in 1876; hat, plaited straw with brim, trimmed with cream silk chiffon and ostrich feathers, worn in 1901 **Provenance** First worn by Harriet Mason (23) bride of John Henderson, boilersmith in 1876 at Sunderland; later worn by daughter, Margaret Henderson (23), bride of Edward Childs, house painter on 27 March 1901 at Saint John's Parish Church, Seaham Harbour, County Durham **Presented by** Miss E Childs (granddaughter and daughter) **Museum number** 1964.838, 839 a - b (CST.952, 953.1-2) ✿

1904
Fabric Ivory crêpe de chine and chiffon **Associated items** Wedding corset, ivory silk satin, trimmed with a satin rosette; shoes, ivory satin, trimmed with ribbon bow; stockings, cream cotton with openwork design; headdress, white heather and orange blossom in silk and wax; orange blossom; coloured silk lavender sachets; four wedding photographs; Ladies Pictorial magazine, with report, 17 September; photograph of entry in The Times 15 September 1904 **Provenance** Worn by Elsie Winifred Gledhill, bride of Reverend Francis Rawson Briggs, of Armitage, Staffordshire, on 31 August 1904 at Saint Bartholomews, Cam, Gloucestershire **Presented by** Mrs J Crowther (daughter) **Museum number** 1979.66.1-5 (CST.2.450-5) ✿

1904
Fabric Cream silk trimmed with chiffon and lace **Associated items** Wide brimmed hat, cream silk velvet, trimmed chiffon and ostrich feather by John Verity, Milliners, Darlington. Copy of wedding photograph **Provenance** Worn by Emma Pickering (34) daughter of Henry Pickering, farmer, Newlands Hall, Frosterley, County Durham who eloped to marry Joshua Raine (39), organist, Frosterley Church **Presented by** Mrs M E Shepherd

(daughter) **Museum number** 1982.8.1
(CST.2.591)

1906-8
Fabric White satin, trimmed with
chiffon and embroidered French knots
Associated items Wreath of orange
blossom; stockings, white silk; shoes, glacé
kid with enamelled buckles; trousseau items:
petticoat; combinations, bed jacket; nightcap;
nightgown, length of lace. Man's tie, black
silk, worn by groom **Provenance** Worn by
bride of donor **Presented by** Mr Hedley
(husband) **Museum number** 1966.94-106
(CST.1134-1145)

1907
Fabric Ivory silk, trimmed with lace
Maker J,T & A Mackerell, Ambleside
Associated items Lace camisole; for the
honeymoon, a tailored jacket, light brown
wool, by Horan Smith & Goulden Limited.
Ladies Tailors, Lansdowne Chambers, 3 St Ann
Street, Manchester **Provenance** Worn by
Mary Ann Thompson, bride of John Robert
Huck, a Pharmaceutical Chemist, of West
Auckland and Barnard Castle on 5 June 1907
at Tabernacle Methodist Church, Appleby
Presented by Miss W T Huck (bride's
daughter) **Museum number** 1962.257-9
(CST.378-80)

1908
Fabric Ivory satin and lace trimmed with
pearls **Maker** F Phaneuf, 141 Bleury Street,
Montreal **Associated items** Photograph
and newspaper reports **Provenance** Worn
by Ruth Sherwood (22), daughter of Colonel
Sir A P Sherwood KCMG MVO, Chief of
Dominion Police, Canada, bride of Major
William Stephenson, owner of Throckley Coal
Company, Northumberland, on 11 June 1908
at Saint George's Church, Ottawa, Canada
Presented by Mrs R S Stephenson (bride)
Museum number 1976.20.1 (CST.2.52)

1909-11
Fabric Three-piece tailored suit of blue wool,
trimmed with braid **Maker** Madam Mollison,
Costumier, 13, Grange Road, Middlesborough
Provenance Said to be the wedding outfit of
'bride-to-be' of great uncle of donor's husband,
which was never worn as she died a few days
before the wedding **Presented by** Mrs
Moore **Museum number** 1966.819
(CST.934)

1910
Fabric Pale blue striped silk gauze over
pink cotton sateen, trimmed with lace
Provenance A bridesmaid's dress worn
by Amy Joanna Somerville Woodiwis (see
her 1913 wedding dress) **Presented by** Mrs
A J Bell (bridesmaid) **Museum
number** 1971.37 (CST.1.7)

1912
Fabric Ivory satin trimmed with lace and
bullion knots **Associated items** Headdress,
artificial orange blossom; separate under
bodice of spotted cotton net; copies of three
photographs **Provenance** Worn by Margaret
Rae bride of James Alexander Fraser on
2 November 1912 at The Carlton, Aberdeen
Presented by Miss M E Fraser (daughter)
Museum number 1980.19.1-2 (CST.2.471-2)

1912 *see page 34*
Fabric Ivory silk satin and silk chiffon, trimmed
with lace, artificial pearls, white beads and
silver metal thread **Maker** Lucile, 23 Hanover
Square, London **Associated items** Veil, silk
tulle; headdress, wreath of artificial laurel leaves
and orange blossom; train, silk chiffon and
lace; court train, silk chiffon, silk satin, lace and
beads; sash, ivory satin and beads. Copies of
photographs **Provenance** Worn by Linda
Morritt (26), daughter of Robert Morritt of
Rokeby Park, Barnard Castle, for her marriage
to William Rhodes Moorhouse, a pioneer
aviator, at Saint Paul's, Knightsbridge, London
References Autobiography by Linda Rhodes
Moorhouse, *Kaleidoscope*, Arthur Baker, 1960
Presented by Mrs Diana Cavendish, Mrs S
Ryle Hodges and Princess Iris Wittgenstein
(nieces) **Museum number** 1989.26.1-5
(CST.2.977A-E) ✿

1913
Fabric Ivory satin, trimmed with lace
and pearls, separate train trimmed with
artificial orange blossom and pearls
Maker Dressmaker in West Hartlepool
Provenance Worn by Amy Joanna
Somerville-Woodiwis, bride of Joseph E Bell,
on 23 July 1913 at Saint Joseph's Church, West
Hartlepool **Presented by** Mrs A J Bell (bride)
Museum number 1971.37.1 (CST.1.6)

1916
Fabric Cream twilled wool tailored
suit, corded silk collar and cuffs
Provenance Worn in Staindrop by Frances
A. Bradley (30), daughter of Matthias Bradley,
grocer, bride of Herbert Storey, son of
Francis Storey, butcher, both of Staindrop,
Barnard Castle **References** Joanna Hashagen,
Wedding Dresses 1870-1930, The Bowes
Museum, 1994 **Presented by** Miss F Storey
(niece) **Museum number** 1968.1 (CST.1362)

1919 *see page 37*
Fabric Ivory silk and wool mix, trimmed
self-fabric frills and machine made lace
Associated items Circular veil of
embroidered machine net; wreath of artificial
orange blossom; shoes, white satin with bar
fastening and diamanté button; stockings,
white silk; handkerchief, white silk with deep
lace edging; length of white satin ribbon
Presented by Mrs Dowson **Museum
number** 1965.154 (CST.1010-16) ✿

✿ SHOWN IN WEDDING BELLES EXHIBITION 2003

1920
Fabric White satin trimmed diamanté
Maker Miss Wilson, 17 Hanover Square,
London, who also made the trousseau
Associated items Shoes, cream satin, oval
paste buckles by Hook Knowles, London;
headdress of artificial orange blossom; original
photograph **Provenance** Worn by Sylvia
Mary Straker (22), bride of Christopher
William Vane, Tenth Lord Barnard, Raby Castle,
County Durham on 14 October 1920 at Saint
Agatha's Church, Gilling West, North Yorkshire
Presented by The Dowager Lady Barnard
(the bride) **Museum number** 1978.37.3, 198
9.39.4-5 (CST.2.364, 2.988-9)

1926 see page 41
Fabric Cream crêpe-backed satin and chiffon,
trimmed with seed pearls and beads and
corsage of artificial roses and orange blossom
Maker Miss Grey Limited, 9, 11, & 13 Brook
Street, Hanover Square, London W1
Associated items Photograph and
newspaper cutting **Provenance** Worn
by Frieda V A Stephenson, of Throckley,
bride of Major John F Lockhart of Hexham,
on 16 June 1921 at Hexham Parish Church,
Northumberland **Presented by** J S
Stephenson (nephew), son of Mrs R S
Stephenson (see her 1908 wedding dress)
Museum number 1979.42.1 (CST.2.413) ✿

1926 see page 41
Fabric Cream silk satin crêpe with lace
yoke and skirt panels over pale peach
silk trimmed with diamanté, pearls, silver
beads and silver lace **Associated items**
Underslip of peach silk, trimmed with broad
bands of lace; copies of two photographs
Provenance Worn by Norah Macoun Wells
(29), bride of Reginald Frederick Spalding
on 15 June 1926 at Hampstead Parish Church,
London **Presented by** Mrs B Westmacott
(Granddaughter) **Museum number** 1993.17
(CST.3.66) ✿

1927 see page 42
Fabric White fine cotton net tunic, trimmed
with silver lamé, over white satin rayon, with
silver lamé belt **Maker** Miss Strand, purchased
from H Binns of Sunderland **Associated
items** Drawstring bag of silver lame; original
photograph **Provenance** Worn by Sarah
Phyllis Hudson, for her marriage to Wilton
Legender Milburn on 8 September 1927
at The Wesleyan Chapel, Sunderland
Presented by Mrs Whittaker (niece)
Museum number 1979.65; (CST.2.449) ✿

1928 see page 45
Fabric Ivory silk satin and silk net, with cut-out
flower shapes with silk net infill, each trimmed
with silver lace and embroidered with bugle
beads and a pearl in the centre of each flower
Maker Norman Hartnell, 10 Bruton Street,
London **Associated items** Train, silk net,

silver metal thread at border, with applied satin
flowers, each trimmed with silver lace and
embroidered with bugle beads and a pearl
in the centre of each flower; veil, silk net, with
band of artificial orange blossom; headdress,
tiara of silver lace, with diamanté and pearls;
copy of photograph **Provenance** Worn by
Joan Redhead, daughter of William Redhead
and Janet, Lady Lacon, bride of John W Ropner,
son of William Ropner, of West Hartlepool
and Thorpe Perrow, Bedale, part of the
Hartlepool shipowning family, on Tuesday,
24 July 1928 at Saint Margaret's, Westminster,
the reception held at Warwick House, Saint
James's, London **Presented by** Mrs J Ropner
(bride) **Museum number** 1981.8.1-3
(CST.2.491-3) ✿

1929
Fabric Dress and jacket of mushroom
brown watered silk chiffon velvet, edged
with silk georgette, jacket with fox fur collar
and cuffs **Associated items** Copies of
three photographs **Provenance** Worn
by Mary C W Willink (31), bride of
Sir Charles Walter Starmer, founder of
North of England Newspapers, Darlington,
on 17 October 1929 at St Bride's, Fleet Street,
London **References** Joanna Hashagen,
Wedding Dresses 1870-1930, The Bowes
Museum, 1994; Karen Baclawski, *The Guide to
Historic Costume*, 1995, pages 228-229 figure
267 **Presented by** Mrs R W Cundall (niece)
Museum number 1980.2.464; (CST.2.464)

1930
Fabric White satin, self belt with diamanté
buckle **Associated items** Coronet
headdress of silk covered loops with attached
veil of embroidered silk net; shoes, white
satin; page boy suit, black velvet jacket,
white satin trousers; original photograph
Presented by Mrs E Evans **Museum
number** 1976.91.1-5 (CST.2.214-8)

1931
Fabric Cream silk satin embroidered in pearls
in a floral design **Provenance** Worn by Ivy
Breckons (26) of Hexham, bride of Michael
Hogarth of Corbridge on 28 September 1931
at Trinity Methodist Church, Hexham
Associated items Copy of photograph
Presented by Bequest of Ivy Hogarth (bride)
Museum number 1989.16 (CST.2.885)

1932 see page 46
Fabric Deep powder blue silk
georgette crêpe trimmed with lace
Associated items Copy of photograph
Provenance Worn by Eva Stephenson,
bride of George G Hankey, farmer, Witton
Gilbert, on 27 April 1932 at Croxdale Church,
County Durham **Presented by** Mrs E Perkins
(daughter) **Museum number** 1998.304.5
(CST.3.202) ✿

1934
Fabric White satin embroidered with beads and diamanté **Maker** J Jones (M/c) Limited, Costumiers and Furriers, 2 Newgate Street, Bishop Auckland **Associated items** Veil, silk net; artificial orange blossom headdress; original dress box marked J Jones; four original photographs **Provenance** Worn by Marion Watson (23), schoolteacher, daughter of headmaster, Wearhead School, bride of Reverend Hector R Stafford of St Albans, Methodist minister, on 4 August 1934 at High House Chapel, Ireshopeburn, Weardale, County Durham **Presented by** Miss B Stafford (daughter) **Museum number** 2003.2333.1-4 (CST.3.283-6)

1934 *see page 49*
Fabric Cream silk panne velvet **Associated items** Dress clip, chrome metal and diamanté; shoes, white satin. The trousseau: matching pyjamas, under-slip, drawers and camisole of ivory satin trimmed with pink machine-made lace. Copies of photographs and wedding certificate **Provenance** Worn by Eleanor J Thomlinson (24), a blacksmith's daughter, of South Hylton, Sunderland, bride of John R Raine, an LNER engine driver, on 24 September 1934, at Saint Mary's, South Hylton **Presented by** Mrs T Hodgson (daughter) **Museum number** 1998.308.1-7; (CST.3.225-31) ✿

1935
Fabric Heavy cream crêpe-backed satin **Associated items** Separate train, cream silk chiffon; veil, silk net; headdress of artificial orange blossom; garter, blue silk, nineteenth century, but worn in 1934; photograph and copy of inventory **Provenance** Worn by Heather Christine Seckham for her marriage to Captain James Frederick Melville Openshaw at Lichfield **Presented by** Mrs F Openshaw (daughter-in-law) **Museum number** 1986.35.2-5 (CST.2.766 a - d)

1935
Fabric White Chantilly lace, trimmed silver lamé **Maker** Madam Lambard, 199, Newgate St, Bishop Auckland **Associated items** Headdress of orange blossom and pearls, silk net veil **Provenance** Worn by Vera Bailey, niece of Madam Lambard, bride of Samuel Charles Pigg, accountant, on 24 April 1935 at Saint Andrew's, Bishop Auckland **Presented by** Mr J Lambard (son) **Museum number** 200-3.2329.1-2 (CST 2.277-8)

1936
Fabric Cream silk velvet **Associated items** Copies of two photographs **Provenance** Worn by Dorothy Emma Raine of Frosterley House, bride of Mr J W Ross on April 15 1936 at Frosterley Church, County Durham. (See mother's wedding dress, 1904)

Presented by Mrs M E Shepherd (niece) **Museum number** 1982.8.3 (CST.2.593)

1937
Fabric Coffee-coloured lace **Maker** Susan Small **Provenance** Worn by Mrs Charlton of Whitley Bay **Presented by** Mrs Charlton (bride) **Museum number** 1963-471 (CST.576)

1937
Fabric Pale turquoise rayon satin, separate belt with diamanté buckle **Associated items** Long matching gloves, ribbon bow, original photograph **Provenance** Worn by Margaret Hall, dressmaker, bride of Thomas Swaddle, joiner, on 17 April 1937, Saint Margaret's Church, Durham city **Presented by** Dr M Swaddle (daughter) **Museum number** 2003.2328.1-3 (CST.3.274-5)

1938 *see page 50*
Fabric Cream lace made of a synthetic fibre, embroidered with silver bugle beads, cream rayon underslip **Associated items** Veil, two layers of silk net, with cream satin bow; head-dress of artificial Lily of the Valley by Halbur Veils, with original box; wedding photograph album and wedding photograph in silver frame **Provenance** Worn by Ruby Pattinson for her marriage to Dr William Stuart Gale, on 7 September 1938 at Low Fell, Gateshead. Dr Gale was a General Medical Practitioner in Teesdale **Presented by** Mr D Gale, Mrs S. Hunter and Mrs P Hopley (children) **Museum number** 1999.184.1-4 (CST.3.235-6) ✿

1940 *see page 53*
Fabric White rayon satin with machine quilted collar and shoulder pads **Maker** Bought from 'Charles', Coney Street, York **Associated items** Veil, white net with chain stitch design in floss silk with applied white rayon satin horseshoes; headdress of artificial flowers and mistletoe, from 'Charles', Coney Street, York **Provenance** Worn by Audrey Grosgert (31), of Ferryhill, County Durham, bride of John G Pattinson, who worked at Trimdon Grange coke ovens, on 20 January 1940 at 3 pm at Saint Luke's Church, Ferryhill **Presented by** Mrs A Pattinson (bride) **Museum number** 1997.12.1-2 (CST.3.149 a & b) ✿

1944
Fabric White lace fabric over white satin **Associated items** Separate white satin slip, bought on coupons in 1943, first worn with black lace overdress to Birmingham Trade Fair Ball (lace was not rationed) **Presented by** Mrs Jackson **Museum number** 1972.103.1-3 (CST.1.246 a - c)

1946
Fabric Pink rayon grosgrain **Maker** Stamp Taylor Model **Associated items** Feather

hat, cream leather gloves **Presented by** Mrs Fairclough **Museum number** 1975.90.1 (CST.1.815 a - c)

1946 *see page 54*
Fabric Ivory rayon satin, self-fabric coloured buttons **Associated items** Two original photographs **Provenance** Worn by Florence Marina Wickham (40), typist, of Thunderbridge, Huddersfield, for her marriage to Arthur William Holmes, an ICI chemist, on 12 January 1946 at Stockton Parish Church **Presented by** Mr R H A Nellist and Mr R Holmes on behalf of Mrs F M Holmes (bride) **Museum number** 1992.14 (CST.3.38) ✿

1947 *see page 57*
Fabric White and silver lamé silk brocade in a floral design **Associated items** Long veil, silk net, with separate short veil; part of train from dress, which had been cut off; copy of a photograph; copy of newspaper report **Provenance** Worn by Anne Milvain, daughter of Lieutenant Colonel R Milvain, Eglingham Hall, Northumberland, bride of Lieutenant Colonel William Innes Watson, solicitor, Spring Lodge, Barnard Castle, on Tuesday 19 August 1947 at Saint Andrews, Heddon-on-the-Wall, Northumberland **Presented by** Colonel W Watson (groom) **Museum number** 1984.20.1 (CST.2.738) ✿

1948
Fabric Lace, machine made with rayon satin panels **Associated items** Two original photographs, original marriage certificate, newspaper cutting and national registration identity cards **Provenance** Worn by Sarah Ann Humble (23), factory worker, bride of Joseph Scorer, butcher, at a double wedding with her sister, Nora, bride of Joseph's brother, William, coal miner, on 10 January 1948 at Saint John's Church, Shildon **Presented by** Mrs M Wilson (daughter) **Museum number** 2003.2330.1-2 (CST 3.279)

1954 *see page 58*
Fabric Cream corded silk with embroidered flower design of pearls, seed pearls, silver beads and diamanté **Maker** Donald Graham, London **Associated items** Headdress, pearl flowers and diamanté, in coronet style **Provenance** Worn by an Oxford undergraduate for her marriage to an Oxford don in April 1954. **Presented by** Mrs H Newton-Wilson **Museum number** 1963-539 (CST.623-4) ✿

1955 *see page 61*
Fabric Cream cotton lace, trimmed with bow and diamanté buckle, piped and lined with cream rayon **Maker** Thought to have been made by the bride **Associated items** Square veil of white net; a Juliet cap of cream velvet trimmed with sequins; shoes, white suede,

open-toed, by 'Merrywalkers'; good luck horseshoe, silver cardboard and rayon ribbon; original photographs, marriage certificate and telegram **Provenance** Worn by Violet Murton (32), a machinist from Crook, bride of Ernest Watson, an electrical engineer inspector, of Witton-le-Wear, on 3 December 1955 at Saint Paul's Church, Hunwick, County Durham **Presented by** Mrs J Hopps (bridesmaid, niece and goddaughter) **Museum number** 1997.11.1-4 (CST.3.145-8) ✿

1958
Fabric Pink nylon net over acetate rayon **Associated items** Copy of photograph **Provenance** Worn as bridesmaid dress by Christine Lowe (11), for her sister Dinah's marriage to William Jones on 5 April 1958 at Saint Mary's Roman Catholic Church, Barnard Castle **Presented by** Mrs D Jones (bride) **Museum number** 1989.15 (CST.2.884)

1959
Fabric White nylon lace fabric trimmed with beads and sequins on deep collar over three full petticoats of net, rayon taffeta and stiffened buckram **Maker** Bought in Newcastle **Associated items** Headdress, coronet of pearls; veil, nylon net; copies of three photographs **Provenance** Worn by donor on 19 September 1959 at the Methodist Chapel, Ferryhill, County Durham **Presented by** Mrs B Stairmand (bride) **Museum number** 1979.6.1-2 (CST.2.410-1)

1963 *see page 62*
Fabric White acetate satin **Maker** Bought from Kendal Milne & Company, Manchester **Associated items** Short veil of four layers of nylon net; pillbox headdress, matching satin, decorated with pearls and rhinestones; copy of photograph **Provenance** Worn by Sandra McLellan of Bramhall, Cheshire, for her marriage to Peter Greenhalgh, teacher at Barnard Castle School, on 17 August 1963 at Saint Nicholls Parish Church, Bramhall **Presented by** Mr and Mrs P Greenhalgh (bride and groom) **Museum number** 1979.52.1-2 (CST.2.427-8) ✿

1969 *see page 65*
Fabric White nylon jersey **Maker** 'The Bridal Shop', Leeds, to the bride's own design **Associated items** Copies of photographs, wedding invitation **Provenance** Worn by Judith Hood, university student, daughter of William Hood, painting conservator, The Bowes Museum, bride of David G Chibbet, who worked at The British Museum, on 26 July 1969 at Saint Cuthbert's Church, Darlington **Presented by** Mr and Mrs W Hood (parents) **Museum number** 1981.53 (CST.2.565) ✿

Right Back view of Wedding Dress of 1863-5 *see page 18*